D0553246

THIS BOOK BELONGS TO

Fireman Sam Annual 1996 is published by **The Redan Company Ltd.** Distributed by **Grandreams Ltd**, 205-211 Kentish Town Road, London NW5. Fireman Sam, including all prominent characters featured in this annual, and the distinctive likenesses thereof, are trademarks and copyright © of **Prism Art and Design Ltd** 1986 and 1995. All rights reserved. Printed in Italy.

CONTENTS

Which Wheel?

One day Bella asked Trevor to go to Newtown to buy a wheel of cheese so she could make pizzas.

"We'd like some pizzas, please, Bella." the twins asked later. "Sorry, I can't make pizza now, I'm waiting for my wheel!"

Rather puzzled, the twins told Sam that Bella needed a **wheel** to make pizzas. So they decided to find one.

Sam asked Norman to find a wheel. "Perhaps Trevor needs to change his wheels so he can go and get the ingredients!"

A listen and Look Story

"Do you know where the spare wheel for the truck is?" Sam asked Elvis, " Bella needs it to make some pizzas!"

Soon Sam, Norman and the twins brought Bella lots of different wheels, large and small. Bella was very confused.

Trevor arrived with a big **wheel of cheese**. "So **that's** the type of wheel Bella wanted!" they all chuckled.

"This is **lovely**," munched Sam, "And it would have been really **rubbery** if you'd used the wheels we brought!"

A Fireman Sam Story!
Skateboard Sam

Sam finds a way to get to work on time!

One morning, Sam woke up with a start and wondered what was wrong.

"I know what it is!" he groaned. "My alarm clock hasn't gone off!" Sam leapt out of bed and dressed as quickly as he could. He then rushed out of the house and down the road towards the Pontypandy Fire Station.

Suddenly, there was a noise like Jupiter's siren. **"Nee! Nah! Nee Nah!"** It was naughty Norman Price making fire engine noises as he came racing around the corner on his new skateboard.

"Look out!" cried Sam. Norman swerved past him. "I'm pretending to drive Jupiter," he grinned.

"Well, you shouldn't go so fast!" cried Fireman Sam sternly.

When Sam arrived at the fire station, Officer Steele was waiting. "Five minutes **late**, Fireman Sam," he moaned. "Don't let it happen again."

"No sir!" replied Sam.

That night, Fireman Sam made sure that his alarm clock was set and working properly. He soon fell asleep and dreamt that he was fighting a blazing fire. In his sleep, Sam knocked the alarm clock on to the floor, but the noise didn't wake him up.

Next day, when Sam opened his eyes, he saw

the broken clock. "Oh **no!**" he groaned. He hurried downstairs and checked the clock in the kitchen. "I'll be late for work again!"

As he hurried to work Fireman Sam saw that Norman had left his skateboard on the pavement while tying one of his shoelaces. Sam stepped straight on the skateboard and took off at top speed.

"**Great Fires of London!**" cried Skateboard Sam. **Whoosh!** He sped by Bella's cafe, Dilys's General Store and the park before hurtling into the fire station. Catching hold of the emergency pole, Sam swung safely from the skateboard.

"Right on time!" cried Station Officer Steele, checking his watch. "Well, that's one way to get to work!"

Norman came running to the station to collect his skateboard. "It goes almost as fast as Jupiter!" laughed Sam.

The Colourful World of Pontypandy!
There is a legend that at the **bottom** of every rainbow there is a pot of **gold!**
1
Colour Naughty Norman's **bubbles** the colours of the **rainbow.**

Follow the strings.
Who is holding
the **red balloon**?
Who is holding
the **kite**?

Which is **your**
favourite colour?
Colour teddy's
balloon in that
colour!

Plant Food!

Norman was in the garden. "Look!" he said to Trevor. "This new plant food is wonderful."

Trevor Evans is a keen gardener and wanted to try the new plant food. He put some in his watering can.

It **worked!** Trevor had never seen such big tomatoes! "I'll certainly win first prize at the Garden Show with these!"

Trevor also tried the plant food in his greenhouse and grew the biggest grapes that he had ever seen!

A Naughty Norman Story

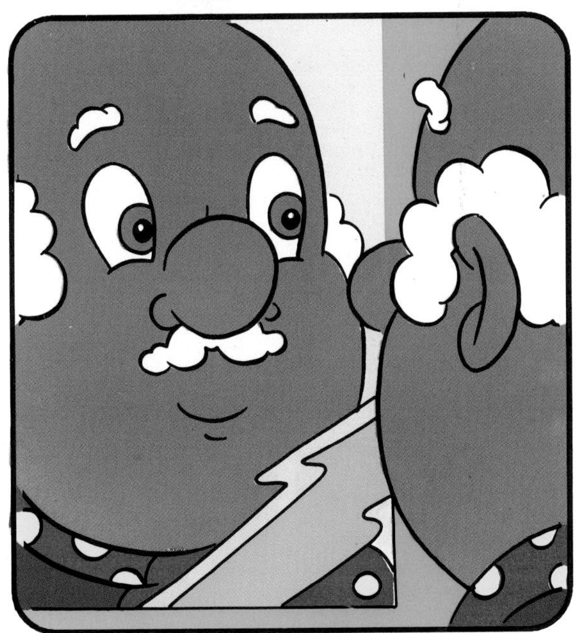

Looking at his thinning hair in the mirror, Trevor wished that he could put plant food on that too!

Norman was in for a shock when he saw Trevor the next day. "What **have** you done?" he exclaimed.

Trevor's hair had grown very long indeed. "It's that miracle plant food," he said sadly. "I tried it on my own hair!"

94/2

"I've cut my hair," laughed Trevor, the next day. "And from now on, I'll use the plant food only in my garden!"

Norman finds himself in the dark at...

The Fancy Dress Party

The firefighters of the Pontypandy Fire Station were holding a fancy dress party.

Sam was dressed as a clown and Bella wore the gown of a beautiful princess.

James has come as a pirate," chuckled Penny. "And so have I!"

"Well, I'm **Quick-Draw Norm**, the fastest gun in the West!" shouted Norman, who was dressed as a cowboy. "No varmit can beat me!"

The party was soon in full swing. Sam decided to entertain his friends with some juggling tricks.

"Watch this!" he said, juggling three balls at once.

Norman whipped out his water pistol. "I'll shoot them thar balls from Sam's hands!" he chuckled.

Splooosh!

The water squirted in Sam's face, knocking him backwards.

"**Waaah!**" cried Bella as one of the balls crashed into her tray of drinks, scattering them everywhere. **Crassssh!**

"**Oops!** The sheriff looks mighty mad!" gulped Norman, seeing the angry expression on Sam's face. "I'd better hide until he cools down!"

Norman ran into the corridor and jumped inside a big metal cupboard.

"Heh! They'll never find me in here!" he chuckled as the door **clanged** shut!

Norman waited until everything had gone quiet but when he tried to open the door he found it was **stuck fast!**

"**Help I can't get out!**" he screamed, feeling rather frightened.

"Great fires of London!" chuckled Sam, hearing Norman's shouts. "I wondered where you had disappeared to, Norman!"

Sam fetched a big screwdriver and forced the lock open. Norman was free again.

"**You should never play or hide in cupboards**," Sam warned Norman. "You could accidently be locked in and no one would know where you were."

Norman apologised for causing so much trouble.

"Not to worry," laughed Sam, handing Norman a big broom. "The cowboys in the Old West used to 'clean up' the towns of bad guys. Now **you** can **clean up** the mess you've made! **Ha-Ha!**"

The End

Santa's
Present
FIRE
FIRE
coloured by

A Bedtime Story

The Snow Robot

It had been snowing in Pontypandy. The snow gave Fireman Sam an idea for an invention. "I love the snow," he thought, "but the roads get blocked and Jupiter might not be able to get through. I will make a **Snow Robot** to clear it away!"

Sam worked very hard on his machine. "It sucks up the snow in one pipe and then sprays it to the other side of the road," he told Trevor who had come to give Sam a lift to the fire station. Norman had overheard Sam talking. While he was away, Norman came wandering into the fireman's garden."What a **great** invention! I'll start it up," he exclaimed, pressing a button. The Snow Machine made a loud noise and rolled out of the garden and down the road. "Oh **no**," cried Norman. "It's **out** of **control!**"

The machine rolled into Dilys's shop. "**Gracious me!**" she cried, as the machine sprayed snow all over her vegetables. She chased it out of the cafe, but it turned around and chased **her** all over the village. "**Quickly!** Telephone for the fire brigade," she gasped. Fireman Sam was in the Crew Room when the fire alarm sounded.

"**Runaway snow machine in Pontypandy**," said Station Officer Steele.

The Firemen quickly drove Jupiter into Pontypandy. Sam pulled the hose from the fire engine and sprayed water all over the machine. It was so cold, that the water turned instantly to ice. The Snow Robot stopped moving.

Sam handed Norman a shovel. "As you caused this trouble, you can clear the roads yourself," he laughed.

Where's Rosa?

Bella was cooking a fish for supper. "Let's go and pick some flowers for the table," she said to Rosa.

It was a lovely day. Bella picked some flowers while her little cat played with the butterflies.

Suddenly, Rosa spotted a rabbit. **"Come back!"** cried Bella - but Rosa chased the rabbit down its hole!

"Oh **no!** Rosa will **never** be able to get out of the rabbit hole! I must 'phone the fire station. They'll rescue her."

A Listen and Look Story

Bella needn't have worried. While she looked down the hole, the rabbit chased Rosa out the other side!

Fireman Sam and Elvis arrived. They dug and dug. "It's no good," said Sam, sadly. "There's **no** sign of her."

Bella eventually went home and noticed that her fish had gone. "Oh **no!**" she cried. "I've been **burgled**!"

Bella soon found the burglar - She was fast asleep in her basket! "That naughty cat has been home **all** the time!"

A Fireman Sam Story!

Norman Hood!

...and his merry pranks!

"I'm going to be like **Robin Hood**," giggled Norman, as he went out to play, dressed in his outlaw costume and carrying his bow and suction-tipped arrows. "I'm going to take from the rich and give to the poor - namely **me!** Tee hee!"

James was eating an apple in the park. Norman tied a piece of string to one of his arrows and shot it at the apple.

"**Hey!** Give that **back!**" shouted James, as the arrow stuck to the apple and Norman pulled it out of his hand with the string.

"I'm a **real** outlaw now," giggled Norman, runnning away from James. "**Everybody's** out to capture **me!**"

Later, Norman set a trap in the park. He tied one end of a rope to the branch of a tree and buried the other end, tied into a loop, under some leaves.

"Now, I have to find someone to walk into my trap," chuckled Norman.

Fireman Sam had heard about Norman's pranks from the twins and went to the park to find him. "**Great fires of London!**" he gasped as an arrow flew through the air and stuck to his helmet.

"You can't catch me, Sam!" chuckled Norman, running off. The naughty outlaw ran away but was so busy running that he didn't notice his own trap! He stepped into the loop of rope and was pulled upsidedown, high into the air. **Twaaannng!**

"**Help!**" he cried. "I can't get down!"

"It serves you right," said Sam, when he saw him. "You don't really deserve to be rescued at all!" But Sam climbed up the tree, and carefully untied the rope. Then he lowered Norman to the ground.

"Your outlaw days are over," he said, smiling, as he led Norman back home. "When I tell Sheriff Dilys what you've been up to, she'll **lock you up** ... in your **bedroom!** Ha! ha!"

Activity Time

Mince Pies
Naughty Norman has helped himself to one of Bella's Christmas mince pies. He has hidden **ten** others in the room. Can **you** find them?

A Journey in Jupiter
FIRE
FIRE
J999
J
coloured by

Activity Time

Find the Cats

Sam has rushed to the rescue of ten cats which are stuck up a tree - but he can only find one! Can **you** find the other nine?

Powerful Polish!

Elvis was having trouble with his cooking. "I'm not very hungry," said Sam, staring down at the burnt meal Elvis served.

"Perhaps you should take a break from the kitchen, Elvis," said Officer Steele. "You could help clean the station instead!"

So Elvis looked in the cupboard for some polish. "I'll soon have this station looking clean," he thought, taking a bottle.

While Sam gave Jupiter a good old wash and polish, Elvis set off to clean the doors to the fire station.

A Listen and Look Story

Elvis scrubbed the doors so hard that he soon felt very tired. "I'm going off to have a little nap!" he thought to himself.

Elvis had been snoozing for a while when Sam called him. "**Wake up!** I think there's something you ought to see!"

"You've used paint **stripper** instead of polish," sighed Sam, showing Elvis the messy peeling paint on the doors.

Poor Elvis had to start painting. But Sam and Steele didn't mind. Bella had cooked them a tasty meal that wasn't burnt!

There's chaos in...

The New Pet Shop

A new pet shop had opened in Newtown. Fireman Sam took Sarah, James and Norman to see the animals.

"What a cute bunny," giggled Sarah when a baby rabbit ate a lettuce leaf from her hand.

The pet shop owner allowed Norman to feed the goldfish and Sam held a puppy as it chewed on its bone.

The Shop owner asked Sam if he would help him carry a big crate upstairs. "It's too heavy to move by myself," he explained.

While Sam was away, the children started to argue. "I want to feed the kittens," shouted Norman, trying to snatch away a bag of food from James's hand.

"No let James feed them!" said Sarah, pushing Norman away. "He asked first!"

Norman fell backwards, knocking into the cages. They fell over with a **crasshh!** The doors burst open and all the animals broke free!

"Great fires of London!" gasped Sam, arriving back in the shop in time to be bowled over by a litter of playful puppies. "What have you three been up to now?"

Sam and the shop owner quickly rounded up all the animals and put them back in their cages.

"Hold on!" said the shop owner, counting the animals. "One of my kittens is **missing**!"

Sam looked outside and saw the kitten which was scampering up a tree.

"This is an **emergency!**" said Sam. "That kitten could fall and hurt itself!"

The shop owner fetched a ladder and Sam climbed up the tree. He gently placed the frightened kitten inside his fire helmet and carried her safely down again.

"Sorry, Sam," apologised the children. "We didn't mean to cause any trouble."

Sam laughed. "It's usually puppies who need to be kept on a lead," he chuckled. "But I think I'll buy leads for you three! It will help to keep you out of mischief!"

But he was joking, of course!

The End

To the Rescue!

Can you help Fireman Sam by finding a path through to the island? But what needs to be rescued? Join the dots to find out!

Now colour in the picture!

Scarves!

Sam was off duty. "Would you like to play football?" he asked the twins. "We're too busy," said James.

"We're busy knitting scarves for Norman," said Sarah, who was making a warm, brightly coloured scarf.

James wasn't such a good knitter. "My scarf is out of shape, so I'm going to knit another one!"

In the cafe, Bella was knitting too. "I'll serve you when I've finished this row," she told her customers.

A Naughty Norman Story

Even Dilys had been knitting in the General Store. "Norman needs scarves," she told a startled Sam.

"What's Norman up to this time?" wondered Sam, watching him carry a big box of coloured scarves.

"I'll follow him to see where he's going," he thought. Norman carried the box into Newtown Zoo.

88/2

The scarves were for the giraffe at the zoo. "It was so cold, I thought that they would keep him warm!"

Activity Time!
Hoses!
Action Stations! Which hose is Sam holding? Is it the top, middle or bottom one?
J 999
Now help Sam by drawing a spurt of water from the hose to put out the fire!

A Job for Penny!

Firefighter Penny Morris had come to Pontypandy Fire Station to help out while Elvis was away. Sam was pleased to see her. Just then, Norman drove into the station in his go-kart. He was pretending to be a policeman and was driving so fast that he knocked over the water buckets. **Splooosh!** Water splashed everywhere!

"Go and play somewhere else!" Sam called to Norman.

Further down the street, Norman saw Trevor coming out of the General Store, carrying a bag of apples. "**Aha! A thief!**" he cried.

Trevor had just bought the apples from Dilys but he decided to play along with Norman. "**Okay**, you caught me!" he laughed. Norman handcuffed Trevor to the lamp-post. "**He he!** This is **mega-brill!**" he cried. But when he tried to let Trevor go, Norman couldn't find the keys to the handcuffs. "Oh **crikey!** You're **stuck**, Trevor!"

Norman 'phoned the fire service. "**Great Fires of London!**" cried Sam when he saw Trevor. "What has Norman been up to?"

"Don't worry, I'll use my big cutters for this job," chuckled Penny. **Snap!** Penny cut through the handcuff links. "**Hurray!** I'm **free!**" shouted Trevor.

Norman had quietly sneaked away. He returned carrying a hose. "Now I've become a fireman! And my first job is to squirt you all!" But Norman got tangled in the hose and squirted himself instead! **Splooosh! "Help!"** he cried.

"I think we'll keep you tied up," Sam laughed. "It will keep you out of trouble!"

Cleaning Trouble

Oh no! Sam's uniform was in tatters!

Sam was about to go off duty. He popped into the Crew Room to say goodbye, and found Elvis carefully ironing the uniforms. "This is taking **forever**," moaned Elvis. "I'm **bored**!"

"That makes you an ironing **board**!" joked Sam, but he knew Elvis had to iron slowly because the tunics were so threadbare. Even Officer Steele had said recently that the uniforms were looking shabby.

On his way home, Sam had an idea. "I'll make a machine to wash, dry and iron clothes in one go. Better for the uniforms - and better for Elvis!"

In his Inventing Shed that night, Sam worked very hard. His machine took a long time to build, but at last it was ready for testing. Sam put his uniform in the washing section, and switched it on. "Nothing more to do," he smiled, "except put on

a clean, ironed uniform in the morning!"

Sam was in for a shock! The next morning, he found that the new machine had been too much for the old outfit! The tunic had shrunk in the washer, and had been torn to ribbons in the drier, while the leggings had been burnt in the ironing section. "It's **ruined!**" gasped Sam. "What will I wear now?"

Just then, the telephone rang. It was Station Officer Steele, who wanted Sam to collect a parcel from Newtown railway station on his way in. Before Sam could mention the uniform, Steele rang off.

Wearing ordinary clothes, a very worried Sam brought the parcel to work with him.Officer Steele was more interested in the parcel than Sam's clothes. He peeled away the wrapping paper - to reveal a **new** set of uniforms! "I sent for them when I saw the state of the others," he explained.

Sam looked very smart in his new uniform. "What a relief," he sighed. "I thought I'd be in **hot water** over what happened, but everything's been **ironed out**!"

Air Pump!

Fireman Sam was busy in his inventing shed working on his new invention - the **air pump robot**.

"It blows up tyres," explained Sam to Officer Steele. "So, it'll be very useful at the fire station."

Elvis had other plans for the new robot. "It can blow up the gym's medicine balls," he said

Later that afternoon, the firemen were having tea when Sam suddenly looked out of the window.

A Listen and Look Story

"**Great fires of London!**" cried Sam. The robot had blown up the ball too much. It filled Jupiter's garage.

The ball became bigger and bigger until it couldn't take in any more air. There was a **terrible** explosion.

Station Officer Steele was very cross when he saw the broken windows. "Your invention will have to **go!**"

82/1

Sam had another idea for his robot. He gave it some washing up liquid to blow huge bubbles for the twins.

Counting Rhyme

Sing-aLong!

There were **ten** in Jupiter and Officer Steele said:
"Move over. Move over!"
So they all moved over and
Norman fell out ...

...there were **nine** in Jupiter and Officer Steele said:
"Move over. Move over!"
So they all moved over and
Trevor fell out ...

...there were **eight** in Jupiter and Officer Steele said:
"Move over, move over!"
So they all moved over and
Elvis fell out...

...there were **seven** in Jupiter and Officer Steele said:
"Move over. Move over!"
So they all moved over and **James** fell out...

...there were **six** in Jupiter and Officer Steele said:
"Move over. Move over!"
So they all moved over and **Rosa** fell out...

...there were **five** in Jupiter and Officer Steele said:
"Move over. Move over!"
So they all moved over and **Penny** fell out...

...there were **four** in Jupiter and Officer Steele said:
"Move over. Move over!"
So they all moved over and **Sam** fell out ...

...there were **three** in Jupiter and Officer Steele said:
"Move over. Move over!"
So they all moved over and **Sarah** fell out ...

...there were **two** in Jupiter and Officer Steele said:
"Move over. Move over!"
So they all moved over and **Dilys** fell out ...

...there was only **one** in Jupiter and he fell out. There was **no one** in Jupiter, so **nobody** said:
"move over. Move over!"

FIRST AID PRACTICE

Nurse Sarah

Sarah wants to be a nurse when she grows up, but who will she practise on?

The Firefighters were practising their first aid. "Can I join in?" said Sarah, arriving in the yard. She was dressed in a smart nurse's uniform. "I want to train to be a nurse."

Fireman Sam laughed. "Of course you can, Sarah. You can start by practising on me."

Sarah had brought along her first aid kit. "I'll pretend you've hurt your arm and bandage you up," said Sarah, as she started wrapping bandages around Sam. By the time she had finished, Sam was bandaged from head to toe!

"**Great fires of London!**" chuckled Sam. "I feel like an Egyptian mummy!"

"Oh dear!" groaned Sarah. "I'm not very good at first aid!" Before Sam could unwrap himself, the alarm sounded! "Come on, Sam," shouted Elvis. "Norman has fallen down a wishing well!"

Sam hopped over to Jupiter, strug-gling to pull off the bandages.

"How did he manage that?" he asked, as Sarah joined them in the cab and Elvis drove Jupiter towards the well. "He was making a wish and leant over too far," explained Elvis. "Luckily, James heard him shouting for help."

Norman was stuck at the bottom of the well. "I **wish** that I was out of here," he moaned as Elvis,

Sam ana Sarah arrived.

"I think that we can make your wish come true," said Sam. "And Sarah's bandages will be very useful!" Sam weaved the bandages into a rope and lowered it down to Norman. Then, he and Elvis pulled Norman back to the surface.

"**Ouch!** I've bruised my toe!" grumbled Norman.

"I'll bandage it for you," said Sarah, and, to Sam's surprise, she bandaged Norman's toe perfectly.

"You'll make a good nurse one day, Sarah," chuckled Sam.

The Naughty Magician

Norman was trying out some magic tricks. "The book says:'place a watch under a hankie, and then...

...**hit** it with a hammer. When you lift up the hankie, the watch will be as good as new!' What a **trick**!"

But when Norman lifted up the hankie he found a very **broken** watch! "Oh **no!** It belongs to Mum!"

"I'll have to earn enough money to buy her a **new** one before she finds out!" he cried.

A Naughty Norman Story!

After doing **three** paper rounds, Norman delivered a heavy box of food to Bella's cafe.

Then he went to the Fire Station and asked for some odd jobs. Fireman Sam let him clean Jupiter.

Norman worked so hard that he soon had enough money to buy Dilys a smart, new watch.

73/2

She was delighted with it. " That old watch didn't work **anyway!**" she told the naughty magician!